THE SECRET
HAPPINESS

JAN GODFREY

AND HONOR AYRES

A long time ago Jesus talked to his friends. They listened to him carefully because he had wise things to say. Jesus told them a secret, the secret of how to be happy…

'People are happy when they know that God is their very good friend,' Jesus said. 'People are happy when they know that God comforts and cares for them when they're hurt or when they're sad. People are happy when they love God and love other people.'

Quiet smiles spread over the faces of the people listening to Jesus. He taught them such good, wise things.

'**Y**ou're all a bit like tiny grains of zesty, zingy salt,' said Jesus. 'A little bit makes a big difference. You're here to make other people happy all over the world.

'And you're a bit like light, too,' said Jesus. 'Shine out like God's good, bright light on a hilltop, so that no one needs to be in the darkness.'

A little boy called Reuben was in the crowd. He imagined God's light spreading everywhere, a light that was bright and beautiful and happy and wonderful.

'Try not to be cross,' said Jesus. 'Don't squabble and fight or call each other names.'

Reuben was with his friends in the crowd. They all looked down at the ground. Sometimes they made each other sad.

'Look after people you love,' said Jesus. 'And don't take things that belong to other people: not the juiciest fruit, or the nicest toy; not a penny from a pocket, not anything at all! What belongs to someone else belongs to them – not to you.'

'Tell the truth and keep your promises,' said Jesus. 'Say YES, if that's what you mean. Say NO, if that's what you mean. Otherwise people get muddled and upset. Use good and helpful words that please God - not words that are rude or spiteful or silly or unkind.'

Reuben thought carefully about what Jesus was saying. He'd once promised his father that he'd help him with his camels. But he'd gone out to play instead. His father hadn't been pleased.

'Don't hurt someone back who's hurt you,' said Jesus.
'Try to be kind to them. God loves everyone the same.
Try to be like him.'

Little Reuben looked at his friends and smiled. He thought
about God loving everyone, good or bad.

Then Reuben looked at a boy who was not his friend. The boy looked at him. Then they began to smile at each other.

'Be kind and generous to people secretly,' said Jesus. 'Don't blow a trumpet and say: "Look how kind I'm being!" Be as quiet as a small and secret mouse. God sees what you do. That's all that matters.'

The people listening to Jesus looked uncomfortable. It was nice when people turned to look when you put coins in a collection tin.

Reuben liked hearing the coins rattle and jangle really loudly. But Jesus said it was a secret between him and God.

'When you pray, whisper secretly to God,' said Jesus.
'Use simple words something like this:

"Our Father God, help us to know you are holy; help us to
be so kind to other people that this world is like heaven.

"Please give everyone enough to eat, and forgive us for the things we've done to hurt each other. Help us not to do bad things, and keep us safe with you always.'"

As he listened, Reuben whispered very quietly to his heavenly father God that he was his friend and he liked him very much.

'Don't keep lots of money and expensive things for yourselves here on earth,' said Jesus. 'Rust and robbers and munching moths might come and eat your special things! God's love is the best treasure you can have.'

One or two people listening to Jesus thought about their money and expensive things, and patted their fat pockets.

Little Reuben thought about rust and robbers and munching moths all zooming into his house to eat his toys and treasures.

Yes, it was best to love God more - and be happy.

'Don't worry about anything,' said Jesus. Birds fluttered and twittered around the crowd of people, looking for crumbs, singing happily.

'Just look at the birds,' said Jesus.

'God makes sure they have enough to eat. If God takes care of those little birds, he'll certainly give you all you need.

'And look at the beautiful flowers around you. They're lovelier than the clothes a rich and wealthy king might wear. God will provide what you need. There is no need to worry!'

'Do you think you're better than other people?' asked Jesus. 'Do you think they're naughtier than you? Be careful.

'Perhaps your friend has only a tiny speck of naughtiness in his *eye* – and maybe you've a great huge log of naughtiness in yours!'

Reuben and his friends giggled and looked in each others' eyes for specks and logs of mischief. They knew they could all be as naughty and mischievous as each other.

'Ask God, your heavenly Father, for what you need,' said Jesus. 'He'll give you good things: not stones instead of bread, not snakes instead of fish!'

All the children laughed. Reuben rolled about on the grass pretending to be a slithery snake.

'God's way can be hard to follow,' said Jesus, 'as hard as squeezing through a little gate. But God will help you if you ask. People who follow God's way will be really happy.'

'You'll know really good people by what they do,' said Jesus.

'A really wicked, wild wolf might pretend to be a sheep – 'but it would still be a really wicked, wild wolf.

'A really good tree will have ripe, juicy fruit on its branches, not thorns or thistles.'

Reuben's friends all snarled and growled at each other and made wicked, wild wolf noises. Then Reuben thought about beautiful ripe and juicy fruit. It was good. Mmmm...

'So... listen to me carefully,' said Jesus. 'Listen and remember. Then you will be like a man building a good safe house on a rock. It won't fall down. But if you forget what I've said, you'll be like a man building a house on a pile of slippery, slithery sand that will fall down with a CRASH.'

Now Reuben knew the secret. Now he knew how to be happy. He wanted to be like the man who built a house on a rock, strong and firm.

Reuben loved his friend Jesus very much.

THE BEATITUDES

Matthew chapter 5, verses 3-12, CEV

God blesses those people who depend only on him.
They belong to the kingdom of heaven!
God blesses those people who grieve. They will find comfort!
God blesses those people who are humble.
The earth will belong to them!
God blesses those people who want to obey him
more than to eat or drink.
They will be given what they want!
God blesses those people who are merciful.
They will be treated with mercy!
God blesses those people whose hearts are pure.
They will see him!
God blesses those people who make peace.
They will be called his children!
God blesses those people who are treated badly for doing right.
They belong to the kingdom of heaven.
God will bless you when people insult you, mistreat you,
and tell all kinds of evil lies about you because of me.
Be happy and excited!
You will have a great reward in heaven.
People did these same things to the prophets
who lived long ago.